WHERE'S SANTA?

IN AUSTRALIA

For Grandpa, Missi and Flash – LS

Scholastic Australia
345 Pacific Highway Lindfield NSW 2070
An imprint of Scholastic Australia Pty Limited
PO Box 579 Gosford NSW 2250
ABN 11 000 614 577
www.scholastic.com.au

Part of the Scholastic Group
Sydney · Auckland · New York · Toronto · London · Mexico City
· New Delhi · Hong Kong · Buenos Aires · Puerto Rico

Published by Scholastic Australia in 2015.
Text and illustrations copyright © Louis Shea, 2015.

National Library of Australia Cataloguing-in-Publication entry
Creator: Shea, Louis, author.
Title: Where's Santa? In Australia / Louis Shea.
ISBN: 9781743626351 (hardback)
Target Audience: For primary school age.
Subjects: Santa Claus.
            Christmas--Australia.
            Picture puzzles.
Dewey Number: A823.4

Typeset in Farmer, Badger, Nemo, Action-man.

Printed by TWP Sdn. Bhd., Malaysia.

Scholastic Australia's policy, in association with Tien Wah Press, is to use papers that are renewable and made
efficiently from wood grown in responsibly managed forests, so as to minimise its environmental footprint.

10 9 8 7 6 5 4 3   16 17 18 19 / 1

WHERE'S SANTA?

Over **700** things to spot!

IN AUSTRALIA

Louis Shea

A Scholastic Australia Book

IT'S DECEMBER AND CHRISTMAS IS FAST APPROACHING. SANTA HAS TRAVELLED DOWN UNDER TO VISIT HIS COUSIN BARRY, BEFORE STARTING THE CHRISTMAS RUN. IT'S GOING TO BE A FLYING VISIT!

Of course he is. Why don't you young'uns go and fetch Santa something to eat. I know he's probably hungry! Hey, Clauso?!

OK, Grandad. We'll make some yummy Aussie cookies.

That's enough Saltymite, Jason.

But everyone loves Saltymite!

MEANWHILE, AS KYLIE AND JASON PREPARE SANTA'S SNACK, AND BARRY AND SANTA CATCH UP ON OLD TIMES, BARRY'S DOG, BLUEY, IS OUTSIDE SHARING RUDOLPH'S MAGIC WITH HIS FRIENDS . . .

Here you go, Santa!

Mmm, chocolate cookies! My favourite.

But they're not choc—

MUNCH!

Here, Santa! Quick! Use the Emergency Cookie Kit!

GLUG GLUG GLUG

WILL SANTA AND BARRY BE ABLE TO CATCH THE KIDS IN TIME? CAN RUDOLPH STOP BLUEY BEFORE HE CAUSES TOO MUCH TROUBLE? WILL BARRY EVER GET HIS FAVOURITE UNDIES BACK?

Can you find each of these in every scene?

Santa

Santa is really busy this Christmas! He still has presents to pack and a list to double-check, but now he has to get Bluey and the grandkids safely back home again too! And all before Christmas Eve! Can you help Santa track them all down?

Cousin Barry

Santa pops in for a quick visit to his cousin Barry every year (usually he comes down the chimney!). Barry's a pretty level-headed bloke, so when he saw his grandkids, his dog and all his livestock fly away, he headed off with Santa to help find them.

Rudolph

It's a little-known fact, but Rudolph's red nose is quite contagious! When Rudolph met Bluey he passed on the magic of his glowing nose. Now Bluey is doing the same to all the animals. Find Rudolph before he accidentally causes more trouble!

Bluey

Bluey is Barry's very friendly red kelpie. He can herd sheep and guard the farm, and now, thanks to Rudolph, he can fly as well! Help Santa and Barry find his lost dog, but be quick—there are flying red-nosed animals all over the country!

Kylie

Kylie was very excited to finally meet Great Cousin Santa; she's been writing to him for years! Kylie was pleased Santa enjoyed their yummy Saltymite snack, but she'll be happy as Larry if he can help her get back home.

Jason

Jason has always wanted to see the sights of Australia! So when the animals flew off, taking him and Kylie along for the ride, Jason couldn't believe his luck! Can you see where he goes on his big Aussie adventure?

Fluffy

Being a yeti, Fluffy's not great in the heat (and he's very sun sensitive). But when Santa was heading off to visit Barry, Fluffy slapped on the zinc and jumped in the sleigh to come visit his own Aussie cousin too!

Bunyip

Most people think a bunyip is a long-lost mythical creature from Down Under. Actually, she's alive and well, and a close relative of the Yeti family. Fluffy sends her a Christmas card every year!

Elvy

Elvy really loves a holiday! He couldn't wait to pack up his toy-making tools and swap his elf hat for one that's better at keeping away the flies. Look out for him relaxing wherever he goes!

Wheelbarrow

Uncle Barry's trusty wheelbarrow is very handy around the farm, but it's never been used quite like this! See if you can spot this unusual sleigh as it travels around the country.

Saltymite

Santa may have thought this Aussie snack tasted very . . . um . . . interesting. But he knows it's not nice to refuse a present, so Santa kindly accepted the gift and brought it along with him. Yum!

Christmas Beetle

Australia is known for its creepy-crawlies, and Christmas just wouldn't be the same without these festive insects. They're everywhere at this time of year! Can you find where this little beauty is hiding?

Australian Capital Territory

Where else to begin the search than in the nation's capital? And just in time for Canberra's hot air balloon festival. But thanks to Bluey, it's not only the balloons sailing through the sky past Parliament House! Can you see which other animals are flying now too?!

Can you find:

12 Red-nosed koalas

11 Spies

10 Giant pins

9 Flags

8 Reporters

7 Marshmallows

6 Skydivers

5 Jumping spiders

4 Sand bags

3 Present balloons

2 Wind turbines

1 Coat of arms

Queensland

The Daintree Rainforest is the oldest rainforest in the world, full of unique and amazing animals and plants. But everyone had better watch out! Some of these plants and animals look even more unusual than ever . . . and hungry!

Can you find:

12 Red-nosed crocodiles

11 Bottles of insect repellent

10 Pineapples

9 Kung-fu cassowaries

8 Green tree pythons

7 Maroon footballs

6 Giant green tree frogs

5 Golden orb spiders

4 Ulysses butterflies

3 Carnivorous plants

2 Umbrellas

1 Tarzan

Tasmania

Over the choppy waters of Bass Strait to Australia's Apple Isle! Famous for apples, yacht racing and chilly temperatures—you may even see an extinct Tassie Tiger if you're lucky. But can you find everyone else amongst the clicking shears and woolly fleece in this shearing shed?

Can you find:

12 Red-nosed Tasmanian devils

11 Lambs

10 Apples

9 Sheepdogs

8 Dingoes in sheep's clothing

7 Red and white jumpers

6 Knitting needles

5 Red-back spiders

4 Old fashioned shears

3 Tasmanian tigers

2 Motorbikes

1 Little Bo Peep

South Australia

To beat the heat in Coober Pedy you have to head underground. There are all kinds of dugouts down there—how cool! Maybe Santa will strike it lucky and find the kids . . . or an opal! There seems to be lots of red noses to light the way in the dark.

Can you find:

12 Red-nosed wombats

11 Opals

10 Marsupial moles

9 Mining carts

8 Giant worms

7 Santa-hat mushrooms

6 Dinosaur skeletons

5 Mouse spiders

4 Torches

3 Windows

2 Pickaxes

1 Golden Santa nugget

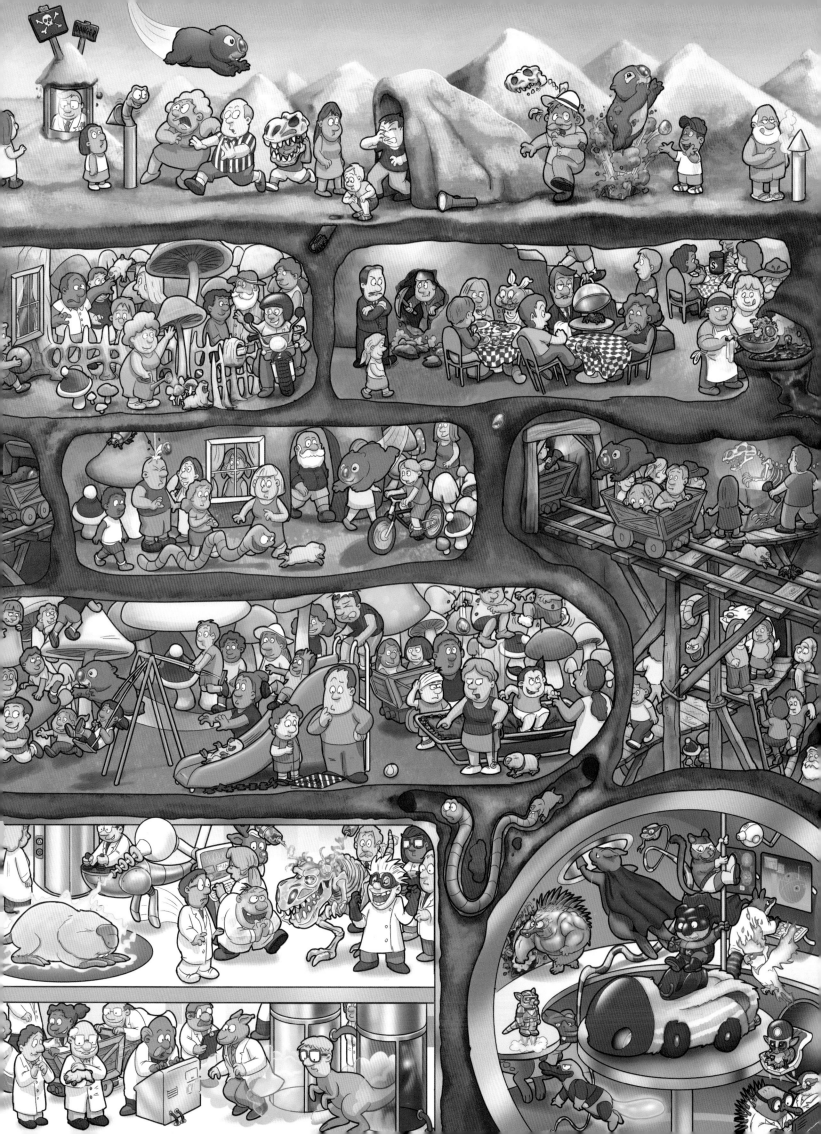

Victoria

Ah, the city of Melbourne, where too much sport is never enough. But it looks like Australia's largest stadium, the MCG, has been double . . . triple . . . overbooked! See if Santa is enjoying the cricket, or the footy, or the tennis, or the athletics, or the car race, or all the rest!

Can you find:

12 Red-nosed possums

11 Meat pies

10 Seagulls wearing scarves

9 Cricket balls

8 Gold prospectors

7 Golden ducks

6 Whistles

5 Huntsman spiders

4 Santa mascots

3 Trophies

2 F1 racing cars

1 Ned Kelly

Western Australia

The Nullarbor Plain stretches for hundreds of kilometres, and this section of the crossing is one of the longest straight roads in the world. It should be easy to spot Santa and Barry in the flat, treeless desert, but today it's unusually busy! What's the hold-up?

Can you find:

12 Red-beaked emus

11 Water bottles

10 Camels in Santa hats

9 UFOs

8 Bearded dragons

7 Wedge-tailed eagles

6 Meteorites

5 Desert wolf spiders

4 Road maps

3 Mirages

2 Santa-crossing signs

1 Rain cloud

New South Wales

Against the backdrop of the famous Sydney skyline, there appears to be a mutiny taking place in bustling Sydney Harbour—animal pirates are storming the ferry! See if you can find everyone in this rowdy bunch, or else they might end up in the drink!

Can you find:

12 Red-nosed dolpins

11 Life rings

10 Cockroaches

9 Fireworks

8 Fruit bats

7 Convicts

6 Ferry tickets

5 Funnel-web spiders

4 Swans

3 Jetskis

2 Opera singers

1 Clown fish

Northern Territory

Christmas is fast approaching so what better place for a bush Christmas party! But will Santa and his helpers be able to find the kids, and get all those red-nosed animals under control? And will Barry ever see his faithful dog (and his favourite knickers) again?!

Can you find:

12 Red-nosed roos

11 Sparklers

10 Christmas crackers

9 Laughing kookaburras

8 Frill-necked lizards

7 Pavlovas

6 Presents

5 Trapdoor spiders

4 Barbecues

3 Brush turkeys

2 Mistletoe

1 Santa's sleigh

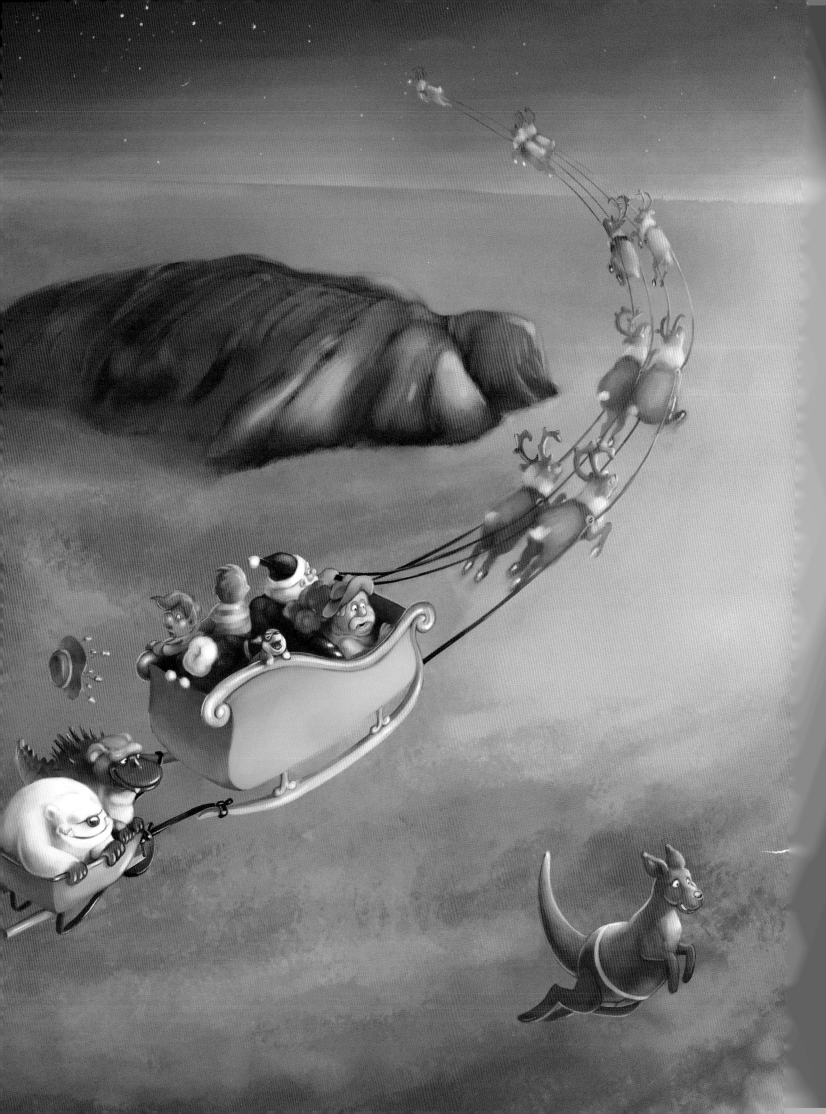